Jackie Jones
LittleSkyBooksSeries@gmail.com
Printed in the United States of America
First Printing, 2021
ISBN: 978-1-7372826-1-7

Little Sky is a small airplane with big dreams. She is not like other airplanes. She has very small wings and a small black nose.

Little Sky wants to fly more than anything. "If I hang around the bigger airplanes, I will learn how to fly more like them," she tells herself. She watches the big planes as they roll down the runway and take off into the sky. "I will learn how to do that," she vows.

She rolls down the runway, next to her house, going faster and faster.

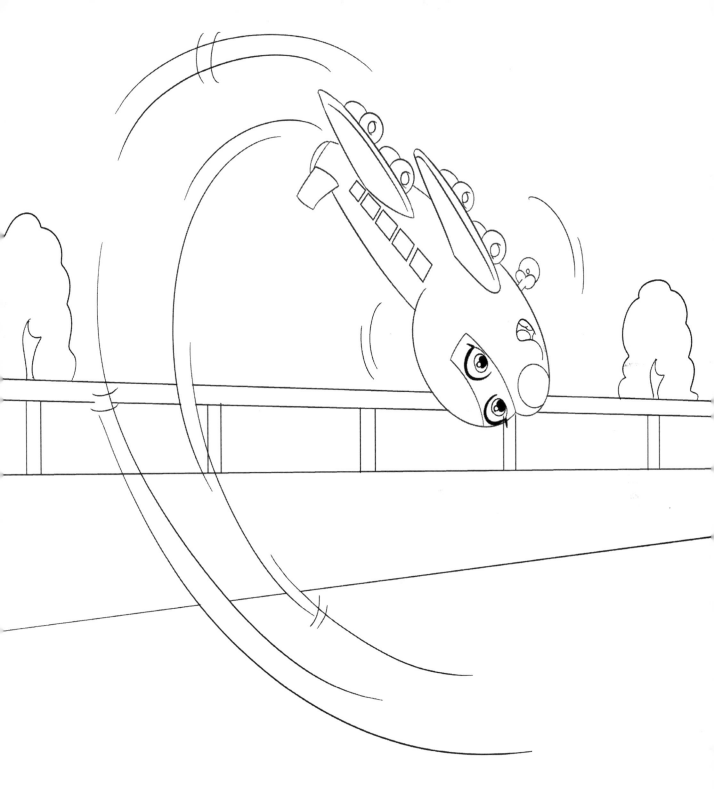

Soon, Little Sky is off the runway. She is flying! However, she doesn't fly very far. She hits the runway...nose first.

Little Sky brushes herself off and sits under a nearby tree. "What's wrong?" she screams out loud. "Why can't I stay in the air like the bigger airplanes?"

"I can tell you why," her mother says as she watches Little Sky struggle to fly. "Your wings are not big and strong enough yet."

Little sky takes a look at her short pink wings and wiggles her
stubby tail blade. "Then how can I get bigger and stronger?"
Little Sky asks her mother.

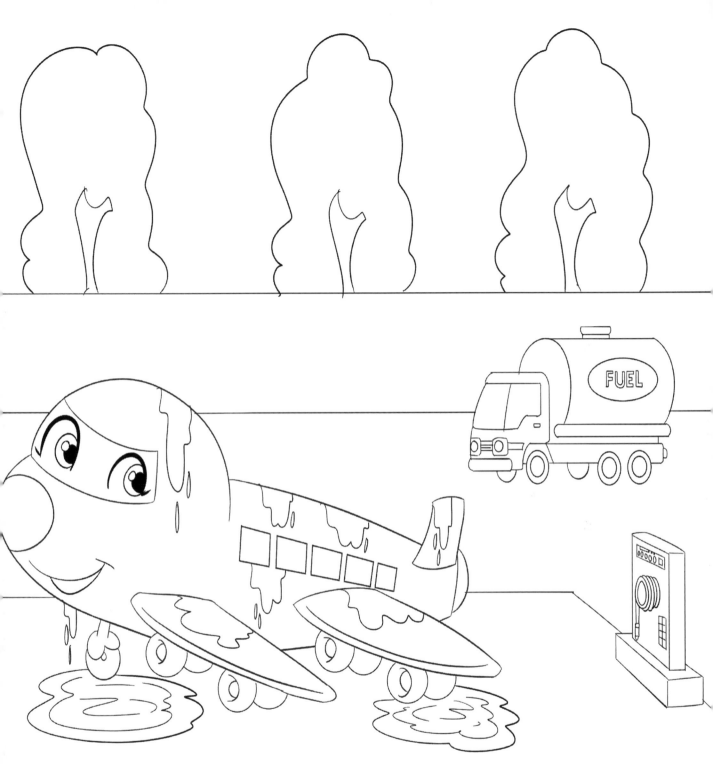

"There are many things you can do," her mother says. "Keep your wheels cleaned, keep your oil changed, and keep gas in your tank. Drink plenty of water and practice rolling down the runway every day."

That doesn't sound like any fun, Little Sky thinks to herself as her mother taxies off. There must be a faster way!

"I know!" cries Little Sky. "I bet I can fly if I jump from the top of my house!"

She knows it won't be easy to get up there, however, Little Sky is very determined! She sees a ladder leaning against the house. She climbs it one rung at a time.

At last, Little Sky reaches the top and is ready to fly again. She takes a deep breath, releases her wheels, and stretches her wings out wide.

She rolls fast, picking up speed. Suddenly, Little Sky jumps into the sky. "I'm flying!" she screams. Then, she lands hard on the ground...nose first.

Little Sky starts to think of other different ways she can fly.
She wants to fly high in the big blue sky like the other airplanes.

"There must be some way I can fly" Little Sky says to herself.
"I know!" she says finally. She knows she will need help flying.

She sees a big airplane speeding down the tar mac and stops him.
His name is Alex. "Can I ride on your back?" she asks.

"No way!" Alex tells her. "You are small, but you are still too heavy. I would never get off the ground with your weight and mine."   Alex taxies off with a loud roar.

"Oh," whispers Little Sky. "Sorry to bother you."

How can I fly under my own steam? The little airplane wonders.
She remembers her mother's advice. Maybe that's worth a try,
she decides.

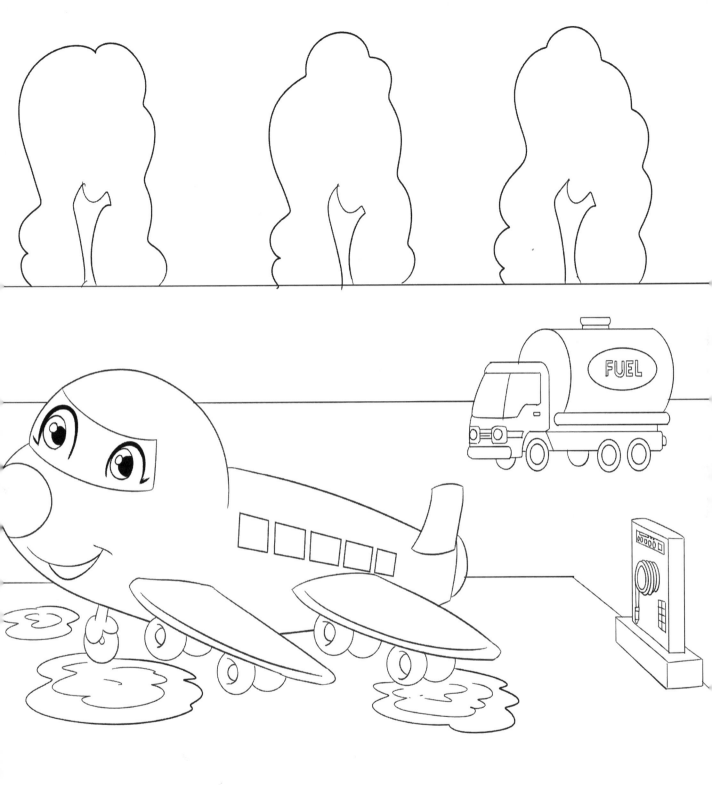

Now Little Sky keeps her wheels and propellers clean and shiny. She makes sure she puts the right type of gas and oil in her engine. She always drinks plenty of water.

She exercises every day, rolling up and down the runway faster and faster. Because of that, Little Sky's wings are getting bigger and stronger.

One day, she takes off into the sky—and stays there! "How tiny the airport looks from up above," Little Sky says.

Little Sky feels like part of the big, blue sky. Her mother watches her fly with a smile on her face. "Go Sky go," she cheers.

As Little Sky comes in for a landing, she hits the ground rather hard...nose first. Although she has learned how to fly, she knows she needs to practice landing safely.

Little Sky is ready to go to flight school! She wants to learn more about flying.

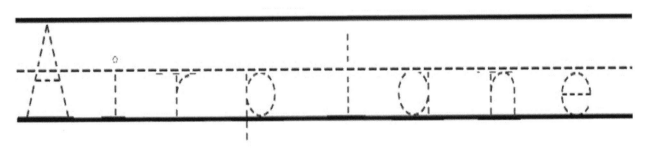

Airplane

House

Tree

Clouds

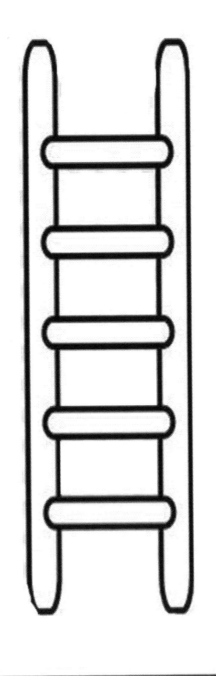

ladder

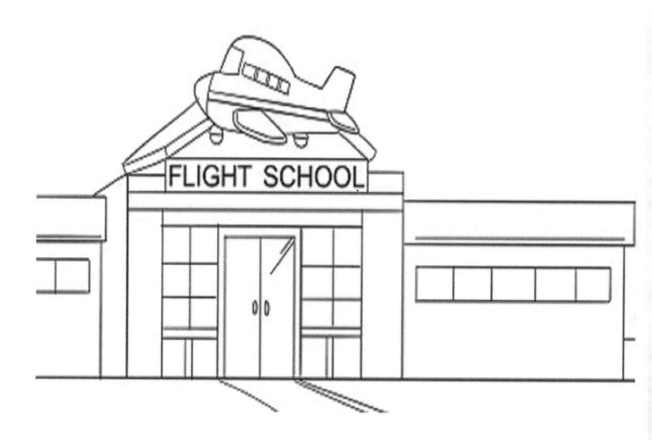

FLIGHT SCHOOL

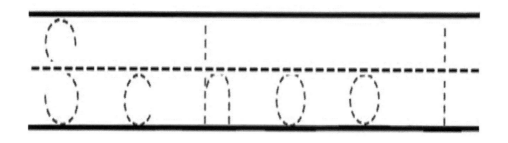

School

R	H	O	U	S	E	M	K	W	A	T	E	R	K
O	F	K	D	C	A	R	Q	G	Y	R	N	Q	P
I	P	T	V	H	Y	A	T	D	L	U	S	M	T
L	B	F	I	O	J	P	R	A	F	B	U	D	U
R	A	E	C	O	U	S	E	R	H	J	P	I	S
A	I	R	P	L	A	N	E	E	M	S	A	G	C
J	P	R	A	F	O	F	K	D	L	W	N	X	K
S	T	D	S	R	H	U	V	A	H	I	S	Q	F
M	R	K	F	S	L	M	D	W	H	E	E	L	S
A	Y	W	B	I	I	D	Q	S	Z	T	A	I	L
L	E	E	A	T	E	D	C	T	R	G	M	C	U
L	C	R	Q	R	C	N	O	S	E	P	W	Q	V

AIRPLANE	JUMP	SMALL
CAR	LADDER	TAIL
CLOUDS	NOSE	TREE
FLY	OIL	WATER
FUN	RAIL	WHEELS
GAS	SCHOOL	WINGS
HOUSE	SKY	

105 Publishing LLC
www.105publishing.com
Austin, Texas

Made in the USA
Middletown, DE
23 May 2022

66102984R10022